The Magic Mirror Book

devised and illustrated by **MARION WALTER**

SCHOLASTIC BOOK SERVICES
NEW YORK • TORONTO • LONDON • AUCKLAND • SYDNEY • TOKYO

ISBN: 0-590-10227-3

Copyright © 1971 by Marion Walter. This edition is published by Scholastic Book Services, a division of Scholastic Magazines, Inc., by arrangement with M. Evans and Company, Inc., publishers of the book under the title MAKE A BIGGER PUDDLE, MAKE A SMALLER WORM.

12 11 10   1/8

To my niece Rachel

who likes puddles

Can you see the whole moon?

Make two boats far apart

Now bring them close together

Can you mend the plate?

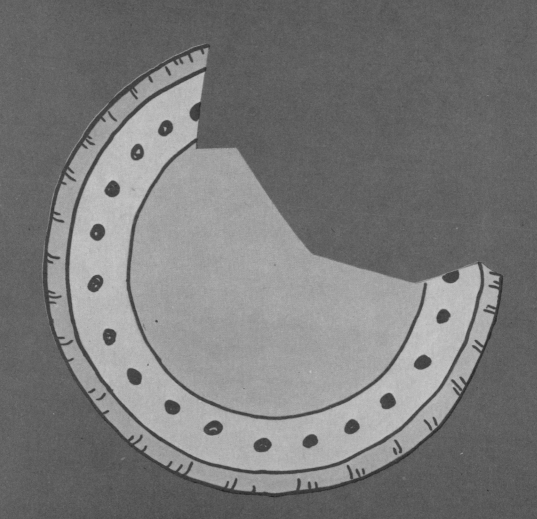

Build a taller tower

    a wider one

       a shorter one

Make it disappear

    and build it again

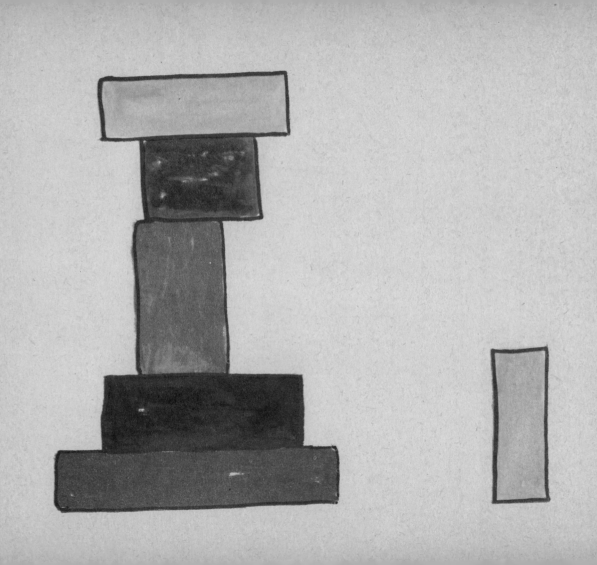

Put some more fish

in the tank

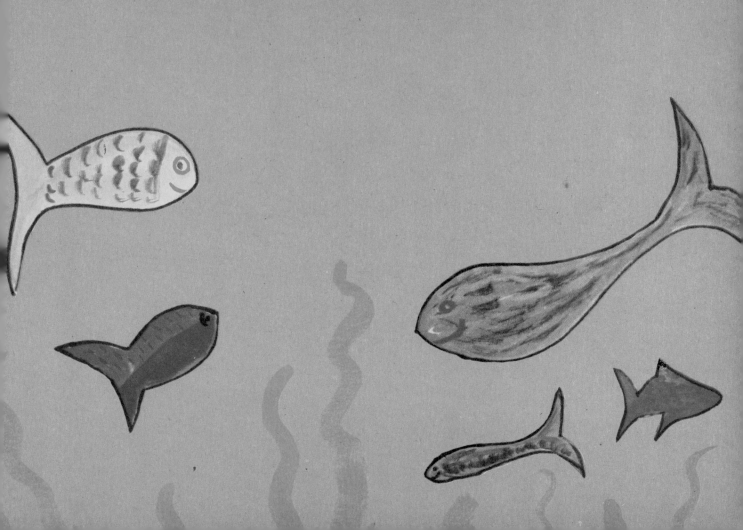

Make a bigger puddle

Make a smaller one

Make a longer worm

Make a shorter one

Make it disappear !

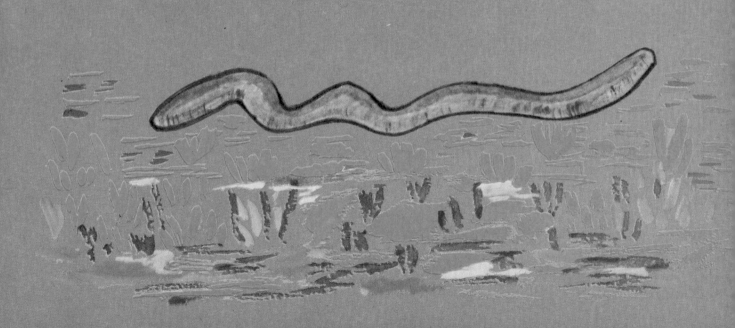

Can you see

another row of houses ?

Can you make longer stripes ?

What else can you do ?

See what you can make

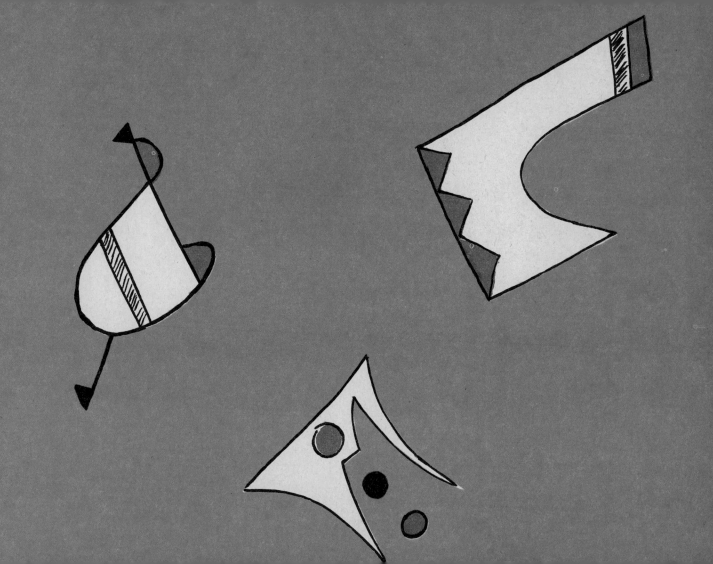

Yellow dots, blue dots, red dots, green dots

Ten dots, nine dots, eight dots, . . . two dots

Many dots or few

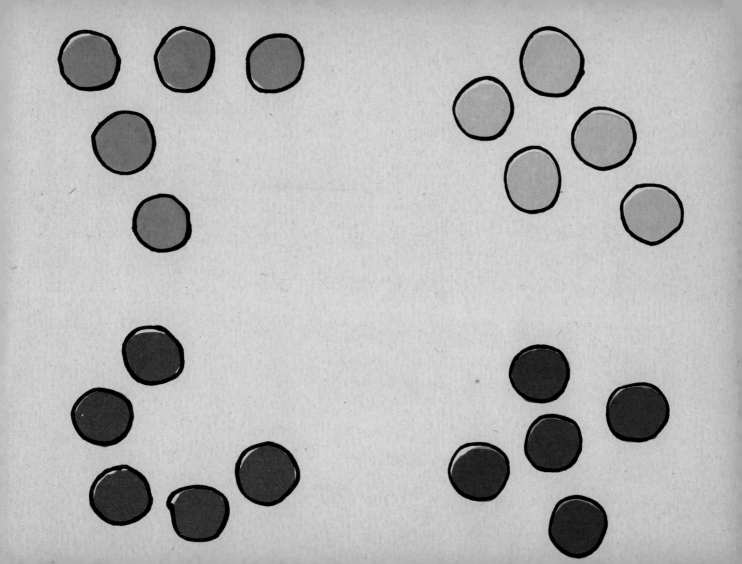

Can you see

the other hand ?

What else can you do ?

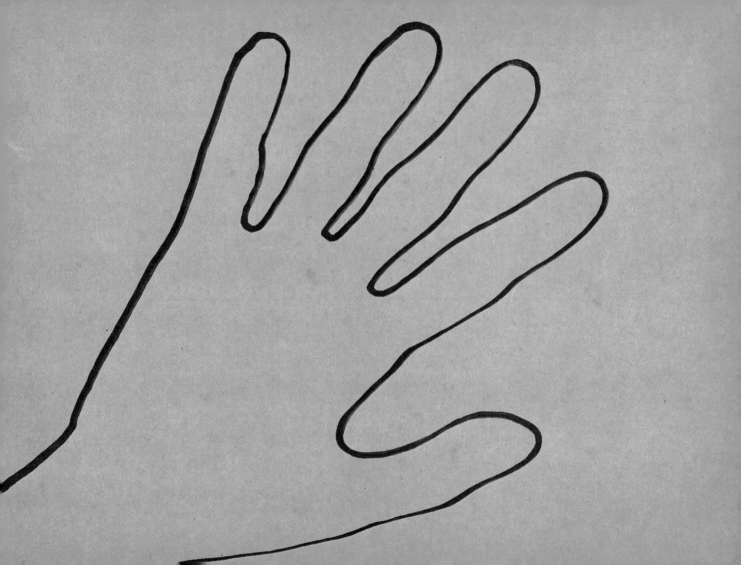

Here is a ghost

Is it fat ?

Is it thin ?

Is it there at all ?

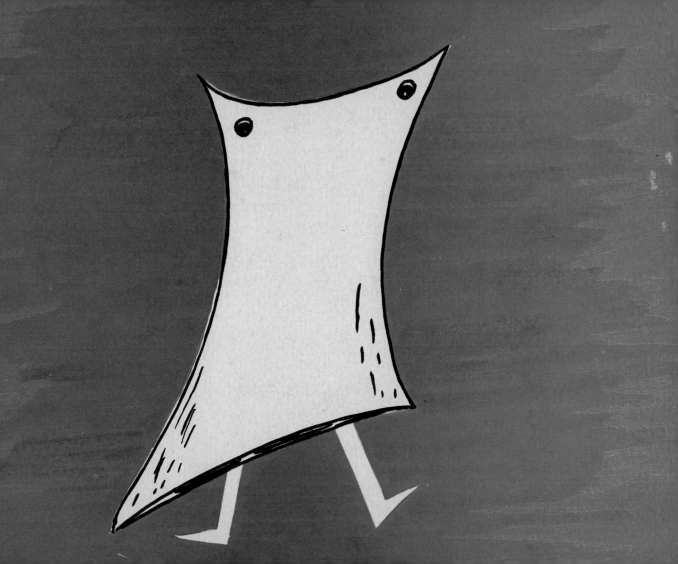

What can you see

in this monster ?